WWE: 2022
A CENTUM BOOK 978-1-913865-79-5
Published in Great Britain by Centum Books Ltd
This edition published 2021
13 5 7 9 10 8 6 4 2

No part of this publication may be reproduced, stored in a retrieval system,
or transmitted in any form or by any means, electronic, mechanical, photocopying,
recording or otherwise, without the prior permission of the publishers.
Centum Books Ltd, 20 Devon Square, Newton Abbot, Devon, TQ12 2HR, UK
9/10 Fenian St, Dublin 2, D02 RX24, Ireland
books@centumbooksltd.co.uk
CENTUM BOOKS Limited Reg. No. 07641486
A CIP catalogue record for this book is available from the British Library.
Printed in China.

THIS ANNUAL BELONGS TO:

centum

CONTENTS

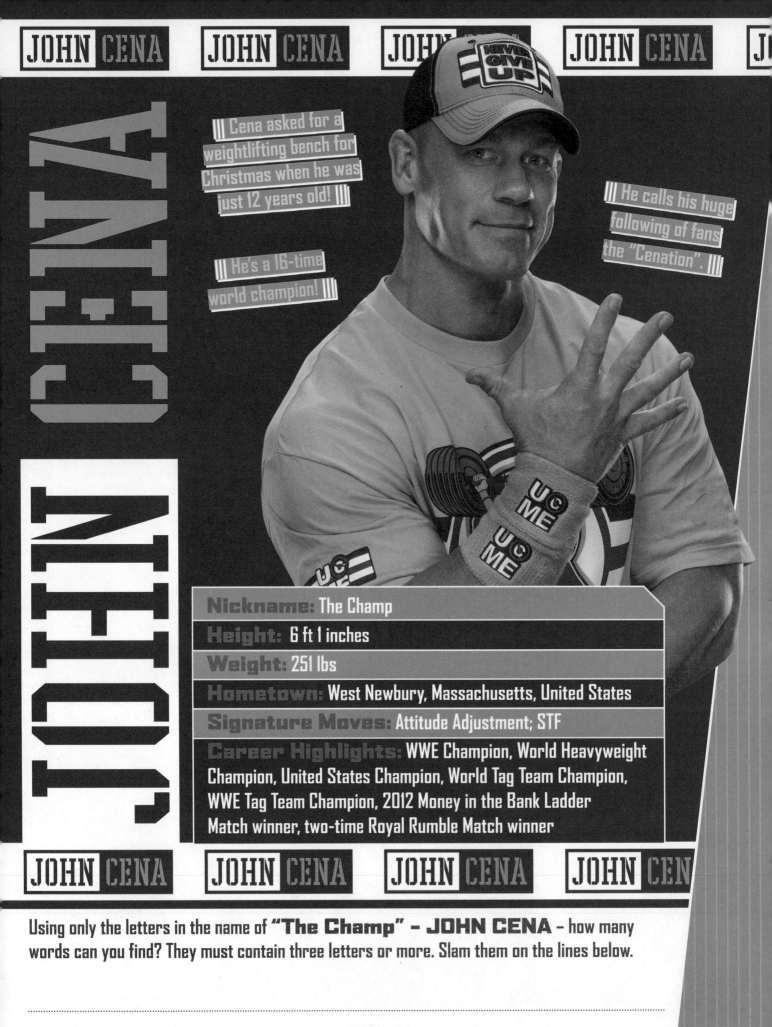

CENA

JOHN CENA

||| Cena asked for a weightlifting bench for Christmas when he was just 12 years old! |||

||| He calls his huge following of fans the "Cenation". |||

||| He's a 16-time world champion! |||

Nickname: The Champ

Height: 6 ft 1 inches

Weight: 251 lbs

Hometown: West Newbury, Massachusetts, United States

Signature Moves: Attitude Adjustment; STF

Career Highlights: WWE Champion, World Heavyweight Champion, United States Champion, World Tag Team Champion, WWE Tag Team Champion, 2012 Money in the Bank Ladder Match winner, two-time Royal Rumble Match winner

Using only the letters in the name of **"The Champ"** – **JOHN CENA** – how many words can you find? They must contain three letters or more. Slam them on the lines below.

CRACK THE CENA CODE

Listen up! This living legend of WWE has spoken many a wise word. Can you smash the code to reveal three unforgettable John Cena phrases?

KEY

A	B	C	D	E	F	G	H	I	J	K	L	M
1	2	3	4	5	6	7	8	9	10	11	12	13

N	O	P	Q	R	S	T	U	V	W	X	Y	Z
14	15	16	17	18	19	20	21	22	23	24	25	26

1

_ _ _ _ _ _ _ '
25 15 21 3 1 14 20

_ _ _ _ _
19 5 5 13 5

SLAMMIN' SILLIES

Q: What did John Cena say to his primary school teacher when she gave him his exam results?

A: You can't C me!

HA HA

JOHN CENA

2

_ _ _ _ _ _ ' _ _ _ _ _ _ _ '
8 21 19 20 12 5   12 15 25 1 12 20 25

_ _ _ _ _ _ _
18 5 19 16 5 3 20

3

_ _ _ _ _ _ _ _ _ _ _
14 5 22 5 18 7 9 22 5 21 16

ROMAN REIGNS

Roman has a famous Superstar family. His cousin is The Rock! Other family members include The Usos, Rikishi, and The Wild Samoans.

Before becoming a WWE Superstar, Reigns played professional American football.

As a child Roman idolised Bret Hart and still thinks he's pretty cool today.

Nickname: Head of the Table

Height: 6 ft 3 inches

Weight: 265 lbs

Hometown: Pensacola, Florida, United States

Signature Moves: Spear; Superman Punch

Career Highlights: Universal Champion, WWE Champion, Intercontinental Champion, United States Champion, WWE Tag Team Champion, 2015 Royal Rumble Match winner, 2014 Superstar of the Year, Slammy Award winner

SPOT UP AND WIN!

There are 12 differences between these two pictures – **can you spot and circle them all?**

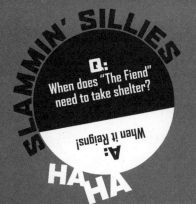

There are 7 words hiding in this grid – can you find them?
– Wreck it and leave!

FLORIDA
PENSACOLA
REIGNS
ROMAN
SMACKDOWN
SPEAR
THE BIG DOG

A	L	O	P	D	L	I	A	E	A
S	G	W	P	H	E	I	R	M	O
M	T	H	E	B	I	G	D	O	G
A	F	A	N	O	K	M	T	R	U
C	L	S	S	K	R	A	P	N	K
K	O	N	A	P	Y	O	R	I	N
D	R	G	C	S	M	E	M	V	O
O	I	I	O	L	W	O	K	A	W
W	D	E	L	M	H	D	K	R	N
N	A	R	A	E	P	S	M	A	E

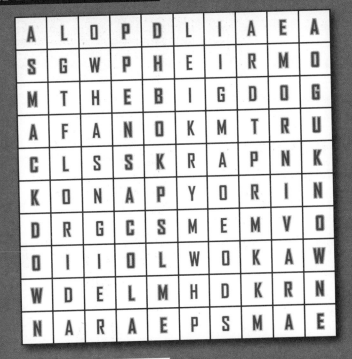

11

ANSWERS: ON PAGE 44

BECKY LYNCH

Becky was the longest-running Raw Women's Champion in history, fending off challenges from many Superstars, including Sasha Banks and Lacey Evans, until her reign ended in May 2020.

She absolutely loves clowns and takes inspiration from them for her performances in the ring.

Nickname: The Man

Height: 5 ft 6 inches

Hometown: Dublin, Ireland

Signature Moves: Dis-arm-her; Man-handle Slam

Career Highlights: Raw Women's Champion, SmackDown Women's Champion, 2019 Women's Royal Rumble Match winner

She's The Man!
Copy the picture of the Raw Superstar into the empty grid, and throw down your best colours.

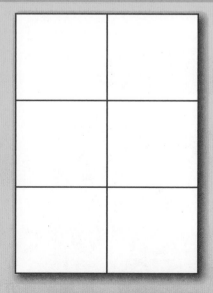

LYNCH THE WORDS

Search out 15 words in this Becky-themed puzzle.
Look up, down, forwards, backwards and diagonally.
Lynch them all!

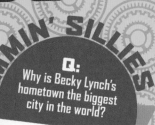

BECKY
CHAMPION
CLOWNS
DISARMHER

DUBLIN
IRELAND
LYNCH
MAN-HANDLE SLAM

RAW
ROYAL RUMBLE
SLAM
SMACKDOWN

SUPERSTAR
THE MAN
WRESTLEMANIA

S	M	A	C	K	D	O	W	N	A	W	D	O	R	M
U	B	W	W	H	P	A	R	D	O	C	I	R	U	A
P	I	E	K	W	A	W	E	U	W	K	S	O	L	N
E	D	A	C	O	K	M	T	B	U	A	A	Y	L	H
R	L	I	D	K	L	A	P	L	K	O	R	A	S	A
S	O	R	K	P	Y	W	R	I	N	B	M	L	N	N
T	H	E	M	A	N	E	W	N	O	S	H	R	W	D
A	O	L	W	L	C	O	A	M	W	N	E	U	I	L
R	O	A	C	O	H	D	K	D	W	S	R	M	A	E
U	V	N	L	W	L	O	K	A	E	N	D	B	K	S
O	R	D	O	W	D	S	L	A	M	I	T	L	E	L
N	L	B	W	R	R	L	B	B	C	R	K	E	C	A
S	A	L	N	W	P	W	A	W	W	E	A	M	S	M
W	R	E	S	T	L	E	M	A	N	I	A	L	B	Y
U	E	H	I	M	Y	S	A	R	C	Y	O	T	A	L

13

ANSWERS: ON PAGE 44

CHARLOTTE FLAIR

Her father is WWE legend "Nature Boy" Ric Flair!

Charlotte is the most decorated female Superstar in WWE history.

She was an incredible volleyball player when she was younger. She won four championships with her college team!

Nickname: The Queen

Height: 5 ft 10 inches

Hometown: "The Queen City" – Charlotte, North Carolina, United States

Signature Moves: Figure-Eight Leglock; Natural Selection

Career Highlights: SmackDown Women's Champion, Raw Women's Champion, WWE Women's Champion, Divas Champion, 2020 Women's Royal Rumble Match winner, NXT Women's Champion, WWE Women's Tag Team Champion

Stun the world and work out these **slammin' scrambles!**

1. NEQUE ....

2. KECGLLO ....

3. BLOVELLALY ....

4. REANTU OYB ....

5. QUORENC ....

CONQUER WITH COLOUR

Add some Queen style flair to this page with your best colouring pens. **You were born to conquer!**

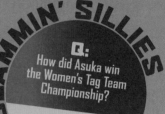

CHARLOTTE FLAIR

ANSWERS: ON PAGE 44

THE ROCK

He's the son of a WWE Hall of Famer, Rocky Johnson.

Despite a hugely successful movie career, The Rock still returned to the ring in the main event of WrestleMania XXVIII against John Cena.

At university he studied criminology and physiology, earning degrees in both – he wanted to join the FBI!

Nickname: The Great One

Height: 6 ft 5 inches

Weight: 260 lbs

Hometown: Miami, Florida, United States

Signature Moves: Rock Bottom; The People's Elbow

Career Highlights: WWE Champion, Intercontinental Champion, World Tag Team Champion, 2000 Royal Rumble Match winner, WCW Champion

How many times can you see the word **"ROCK"** in this letter grid? Look up, down, diagonally, forwards and backwards. It doesn't matter how you do it – just **circle them all!**

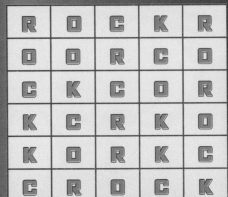

R	O	C	K	R
O	O	R	C	O
C	K	C	O	R
K	C	R	K	O
K	O	R	K	C
C	R	O	C	K

ROCK ROCK ROCK ROCK

16

WHICH IS THE GREAT ONE?

Only one of these silhouettes is the real Rock.
Can you find him? Just bring it!

ANSWERS: ON PAGE 44

CATCHPHRASE:
"THE JABRONI-BEATIN', PIE-EATIN', TRAILBLAZIN' PEOPLE'S CHAMP!"

CATCHPHRASE:
"IT DOESN'T MATTER WHAT YOUR NAME IS."

CATCHPHRASE:
"CAN YOU SMELL WHAT THE ROCK IS COOKING?"

KEEP IT *IN THE* FAMILY

WWE features some formidably talented famous families, with sons, daughters and cousins following in the footsteps of their Superstar relatives. Can you **match up** the four pairs of related stars? **Write your answers in the box.**

___ _____ & _____ _____
[father and daughter]

___ ____ & ____ _____
[cousins]

____ ____ & _____
[uncle and niece]

DREW McINTYRE

III Drew started training to become a WWE Superstar when he was just 15 years old! III

III He defeated Brock Lesnar at the main event of WrestleMania 36 to capture his first WWE Championship. III

III He has a master's degree in criminology from Glasgow Caledonian University. III

Nickname: The Scottish Warrior

Height: 6 ft 5 inches

Weight: 265 lbs

Hometown: Ayr, Scotland

Signature Move: Claymore

Career Highlights: WWE Champion, 2020 Men's Royal Rumble Match winner, Intercontinental Champion, WWE Tag Team Champion, Raw Tag Team Champion, NXT Champion, Raw's Gold Medal of Excellence

McIntyre might not like maths, but do you? The number in each square below is equal to the sum of the numbers in the circles on either side of it. **Fill in the missing numbers!**

14 13   15 10   7 5   9 8

9   9   6   3

TALK LESS, CLAYMORE!

Drew is never afraid to drop any opponent with his signature move.
Help him find the path to his rival through the grid by following the word **CLAYMORE** three times.

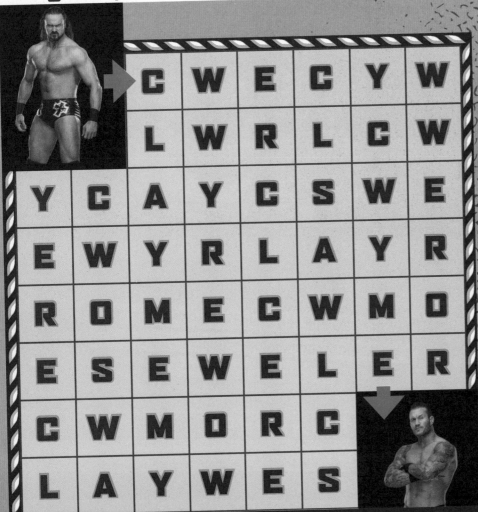

SLAMMIN' SILLIES

Q: Why did Drew McIntyre prefer pottery to maths?

A: Because he liked playing with clay more!

HA HA

His catchphrase might say "talk less", but McIntyre has said a few famous things in his time. Which two of these do you think are genuine quotes from the Scottish Warrior?
Put a tick next to your answers.

1 "I am happy to do anything that comes my way, and I will always do my best in anything that presents itself."

2 "Failure's not an option. It's just a step."

3 "All success begins with self-discipline. It starts with you."

4 "I want to inspire people and show people no matter what happens, no matter how much you get knocked down, you can pick yourself up. Just keep pushing forward, keep being positive."

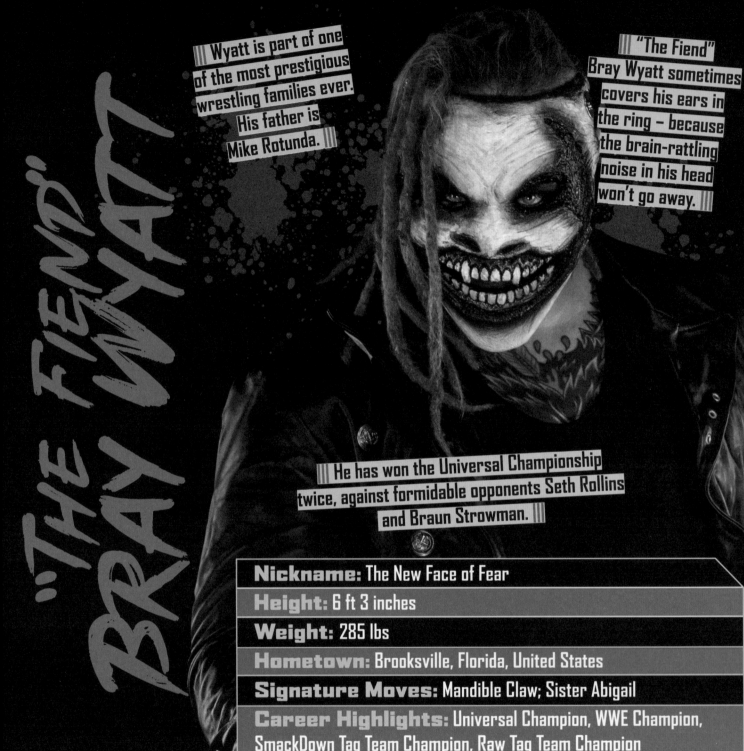

"THE FIEND" BRAY WYATT

Wyatt is part of one of the most prestigious wrestling families ever. His father is Mike Rotunda.

"The Fiend" Bray Wyatt sometimes covers his ears in the ring – because the brain-rattling noise in his head won't go away.

He has won the Universal Championship twice, against formidable opponents Seth Rollins and Braun Strowman.

Nickname: The New Face of Fear

Height: 6 ft 3 inches

Weight: 285 lbs

Hometown: Brooksville, Florida, United States

Signature Moves: Mandible Claw; Sister Abigail

Career Highlights: Universal Champion, WWE Champion, SmackDown Tag Team Champion, Raw Tag Team Champion

If you had a **scary alter-ego,** who would they be?

ALTER-EGO NAME: _____

CATCHPHRASE TO SCARE YOUR OPPONENTS:

_____

_____

DRAW A FEARSOME MASK TO WEAR TO HIDE YOUR TRUE IDENTITY:

SUPERSTAR SCRAMBLE

Can you **unscramble the names** of The Fiend's biggest ring rivals?

1 HONJ AENC

_ _ _ _ _ _ _ _ _

2 NORMA GIRENS

_ _ _ _ _ _ _ _ _ _ _

3 NEKA

_ _ _ _

4 TEHS LORINLS

_ _ _ _ _ _ _ _ _ _

5 NARUB MTORSANW

_ _ _ _ _ _ _ _ _ _ _ _

6 DRANY TOORN

_ _ _ _ _ _ _ _ _ _

7 JA LETSSY

_ _ _ _ _ _ _

8 VEINK NOEWS

_ _ _ _ _ _ _ _ _ _

ANSWERS: ON PAGE 44

ALEXA BLISS

In her first year in WWE, she became the first Superstar to win both the SmackDown Women's Championship and the Raw Women's Championship.

Her favourite band, Bowling for Soup, wrote a song about her!

Alexa hosts her own talk show, "A Moment of Bliss".

Alexa became enchanted by "The Fiend" Bray Wyatt in 2020 and has become his full-blown accomplice!

Nickname: Five Feet of Fury

Height: 5 ft 1 inch

Hometown: Columbus, Ohio, United States

Signature Move: Twisted Bliss

Career Highlights: Raw Women's Champion, SmackDown Women's Champion, WWE Women's Tag Team Champion, 2018 Women's Money in the Bank Ladder Match winner

If your favourite band wrote a song about you, what would the lyrics be?
Would they rhyme with your name? **Try some out below.**

....

....

....

DOUBLE BLISS

Can you create some Alexa-style awesomeness by **creating a double of her blissful badge** and matching the colours, too?

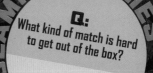

SLAMMIN' SILLIES

Q: What kind of match is hard to get out of the box?

A: A WWE match!

HA HA

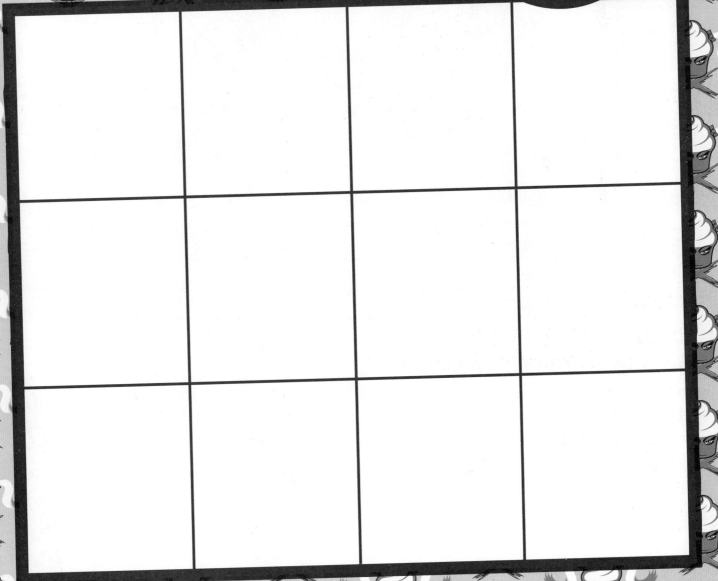

BIANCA BELAIR

She uses her long hair braid to whip her opponents to shreds!

Before joining WWE, Belair earned several awards in track-and-field at the University of Tennessee.

In the 2020 Women's Royal Rumble Match, she lasted more than 33 minutes and eliminated eight competitors!

CATCHPHRASE:
"I go here now!"

Nickname: Est of WWE (strongEST, fastEST, toughEST and all-around bEST)

Height: 5 ft 7 inches

Hometown: Knoxville, Tennessee, United States

Signature move: K.O.D (Kiss of Death)

Career Highlights: Royal Rumble Match winner, SmackDown Women's Champion

Uncover these **great-EST** hidden words by **linking the letters in each circle**, one by one, across the centre. Link the final letter of the word back with the first letter. Once you've made a clean finish, you will have drawn a super star. **Go here now!**

START HERE

1 s k d n m o c w a

2 START HERE n s g t a o s p r e

3 START HERE k v l e n x l t o o

TRU**EST** OR FALS**EST**?

How much do you know about this great**EST** Superstar?
Cover up her profile on the previous page (only some of the answers are there), then
choose **"TRUE"** or **"FALSE"** for the statements below by circling your answer.

1 BIANCA IS FROM FLORIDA. **TRUE** **FALSE**

2 SHE TAUNTS HER OPPONENTS WITH THE WORDS "I GO HERE NOW". **TRUE** **FALSE**

3 BEFORE JOINING WWE, SHE WAS AN AMAZING TRACK-AND-FIELD ATHLETE AT HER UNIVERSITY. **TRUE** **FALSE**

4 SHE IS OVER 6 FEET TALL. **TRUE** **FALSE**

5 SHE WON THE WOMEN'S ROYAL RUMBLE MATCH IN 2021. **TRUE** **FALSE**

6 SHE IS RIC FLAIR'S DAUGHTER. **TRUE** **FALSE**

7 AT *WRESTLEMANIA 36*, SHE LENT A HELPING HAND TO TAG TEAM THE STREET PROFITS. **TRUE** **FALSE**

8 HER SIGNATURE MOVE IS THE CLAYMORE. **TRUE** **FALSE**

THE ULTIMATE WWE QUIZ

How much do you really know about the WWE Universe? Test yourself then your friends with this ultimate quiz. **Circle your answer for each question.**

1 What is the name of the Friday night WWE television show?

Raw
SmackDown
NXT
WrestleMania

The Rock
Ultimate Warrior
Undertaker
Bret "Hit Man" Hart

The Tombstone is a signature move of which legendary Superstar? **2**

3 What country is Becky Lynch from?

Ireland
Scotland
England
Canada

Edge
"Stone Cold" Steve Austin
John Cena
Finn Bálor

Who was the first person to become WWE Universal Champion? **4**

5 What is the name of the Monday night WWE television show?

Raw
SmackDown
NXT
WrestleMania

John Cena
Roman Reigns
Becky Lynch
Sasha Banks

Which Superstar is known as "The Man"? **6**

7 Which Superstar is cousin to Dwayne "The Rock" Johnson?

Charlotte Flair
Edge
Bianca Belair
Roman Reigns

Claymore
Mandible Claw
Big Ending
Stomp

What is "The Scottish Warrior" Drew McIntyre's signature move? **8**

9 "The Fiend" is the alter-ego of which Superstar?

Asuka
Bray Wyatt
Bret "Hit Man" Hart
Alexa Bliss

Ric Flair
Shawn Michaels
"Stone Cold" Steve Austin
Randy Savage

Who was the first Superstar to ever escape The Rock's finisher move, The Rock Bottom? **10**

ANSWERS: ON PAGE 45

BRET "HIT MAN" HART

||| Hart won his first WWE Championship in a non-televised live event in Saskatoon, Saskatchewan, Canada, beating Ric Flair. |||

||| He was once in a tag team with his brother-in-law, Jim "The Anvil" Neidhart. They were called The Hart Foundation and won the World Tag Team Championship twice! |||

||| After a long absence, Hart returned to WWE in 2010 and finally defeated his biggest rival, Mr. McMahon, with help from many members of his family. |||

Nickname: The Excellence of Execution
Height: 6 ft
Weight: 235 lbs
Hometown: Calgary, Alberta, Canada
Signature Moves: The Sharpshooter; Hart Attack
Career Highlights: WWE Champion; Intercontinental Champion; World Tag Team Champion; King of the Ring; two-time Royal Rumble Match winner; United States Champion; WCW Tag Team Champion; WCW Champion; Raw General Manager; Two-time WWE Hall of Fame Inductee (Class of 2006 & 2019)

Bret "Hit Man" Hart is everywhere in the ring – there's no escaping his Excellence of Execution! How many times can you find his surname, **HART**, in the grid? Look up, down, diagonally, backwards and forwards. **Circle them all.**

H	T	H	A	R	T
T	H	A	R	T	R
T	R	R	H	R	A
R	A	T	R	A	H

REVEAL THE AWESOMENESS

Cross out every **W** and **M** below to reveal another nickname used for the legendary **Bret "Hit Man" Hart.**

W	M	W	M	T	M	W	M	W	M
M	W	H	W	M	W	M	W	M	E
W	W	M	W	W	M	W	W	M	W
M	W	B	M	W	W	M	E	W	M
S	M	M	W	T	W	M	W	M	W
M	W	M	W	M	M	W	W	T	W
W	M	H	W	M	W	M	W	M	M
M	W	M	W	E	M	W	M	R	W
W	M	W	W	W	M	E	W	M	M
M	W	M	I	W	M	W	W	S	W

‗ ‗ ‗ ‗ ‗ ‗ ‗ ‗ ‗

‗ ‗ ‗ ‗ ‗ ‗ ‗ ‗

Now cross out every **B** and **D** in this grid to reveal the name of one of **Hit Man's biggest rivals.**

‗ ‗ ‗ ‗ ‗ ‗

‗ ‗ ‗ ‗ ‗

B	B	D	B	D	D	B	D	B	D
B	D	B	D	D	B	D	A	D	B
D	M	D	S	B	D	B	B	D	B
E	D	B	D	B	B	B	D	I	D
D	B	B	B	D	D	B	D	D	B
H	D	B	B	D	B	B	L	D	B
B	D	B	C	D	N	D	B	B	D
B	A	B	D	B	D	D	B	S	B
B	D	B	D	D	B	D	D	B	B
W	B	D	B	D	D	D	B	D	B	H

ANSWERS: ON PAGE 45

31

RANDY SAVAGE

MACHO MAN

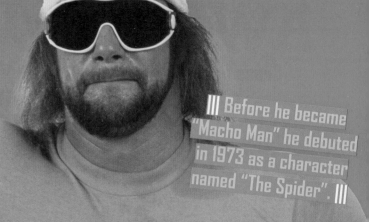

III His entrance music was called "Pomp and Circumstance" – totally suiting his style! III

III Before he became "Macho Man" he debuted in 1973 as a character named "The Spider". III

III "Macho Man" almost became a Major League Baseball player, but an injury to his arm meant he switched to WWE instead. III

Nickname: Macho Man

Height: 6 ft 2 inches

Weight: 237 lbs

Hometown: Sarasota, Florida, United States

Signature Move: Elbow drop off the top rope

Career Highlights: WWE Champion, World Heavyweight Champion, Intercontinental Champion, married Miss Elizabeth at SummerSlam 1991, 2015 WWE Hall of Fame Inductee

Answer the clues to **fill in this word grid.** Once you've finished, Macho Man's hometown will be revealed in the centre column.

1. Macho Man's original nickname was The _ _ _ _ _ _ . [6]
2. What is Macho Man's last name? [6]
3. What is his first name? [5]
4. What sport did he play before entering WWE? [8]
5. Macho Man called himself the "_ _ _ _ there is". [4]
6. His signature move is the "_ _ _ _ _ drop of the top rope". [5]
7. He was "too _ _ _ _ to handle". [3]
8. His home country was the United _ _ _ _ _ _ . [6]

MACHO MAZE!

Oooh yeah! Macho Man is on his way to the ring to defeat his rival, but which path will get him there?

MACHO MAN RANDY SAVAGE

FAMOUS QUOTES:

"Too hot to handle, too cold to hold!"

FAMOUS QUOTES:

"Best there is ... past, present and future! Ooooh yeeeah!"

Can you spot **6 differences** between these two pictures? **Circle them all!**

33

ANSWERS: ON PAGE 45

"STONE COLD" STEVE AUSTIN

He was the first Superstar to ever escape The Rock's signature move, The Rock Bottom, at WrestleMania XV.

His entrance always began with the signature sound of shattering glass – everyone knew what was coming!

He joined WWE in January 1996 as Ted DiBiase's "Million Dollar Champion".

He had a big rivalry with The Rock – they headlined three WrestleMania matches together from 1999 to 2003.

SLAMMIN' SILLIES
HA HA

Q: How does Steve Austin like his ice cream?

A: Stone Cold!

Nickname: The Texas Rattlesnake

Height: 6 ft 2 inches

Weight: 252 lbs

Hometown: Victoria, Texas, United States

Signature Move: Stone Cold Stunner

Career Highlights: WWE Champion; Intercontinental Champion; World Tag Team Champion; 1996 King of the Ring; Royal Rumble Match winner (1997, 1998, 2001); WCW U.S. Champion; WCW Tag Team Champion; 2009 WWE Hall of Fame Inductee

Which of these is the **real** "Stone Cold" Steve Austin? **Slam a circle around your answer.**

1 STONE COLD STEVE AUSTIN

2 STONE COLD STEVE AUSTIN

3 STONE COLD STEVE AUSTIN

'COS STONE COLD SAID SO!

"Stone Cold" is famous for getting people to do things "because he said so. "But which of these quotes did the legendary Superstar **actually** say? Tick the ones you think are right, then check the answer page.

1 "I can drive anything on wheels... I can drive anything, actually."

2 "With drive and a bit of talent you can move mountains."

3 "Live strong, act bold, be brave. Nothing's hard to do, ALWAYS BELIEVE."

4 "I eat so much chicken, I'm surprised I haven't grown feathers yet."

5 "Tune in next week, same Stone Cold time, same Stone Cold channel."

6 "Nobody remembers second place"

7 "If your goal isn't to be on top, then you don't deserve to be here."

ANSWERS: ON PAGE 45

DEFEAT *THE* DIFFERENCES

Superstars Daniel Bryan and Sami Zayn face each other once again in the *WrestleMania* ring! Can you find and circle **10 differences** in the two pictures below?

① V'S

② V'S

||| Sami Zayn defeated Daniel Bryan on Night 1 of WrestleMania 36 to retain the Intercontinental Championship! |||

||| Bryan attempted an attack off the top rope, but Zayn countered into a modified version of Helluva Kick for the win. |||

DEFEAT THE DIFFERENCES

Bianca Belair takes on Bayley in an epic match! Can you spot **10 differences** in the second picture below?

1

KNOW YOUR ROLE... MODEL
BAY LEY
VS
BIANCA BELAIR

2

KNOW YOUR ROLE... MODEL
BEY LEY
VS
BIANCA BBLAIR

The powerful pair met in a mighty SmackDown match in January 2021.

Bayley held Bianca in a tabletop cover, but Bianca broke out and issued her new finisher, the Kiss of Death. She covered Bayley to claim the win.

ANSWERS: ON PAGE 45

1CON1C

Do you know the Superstar names of these **WWE icons?**
Write the correct name for each Superstar under their image.

1

2

3

?

4

5

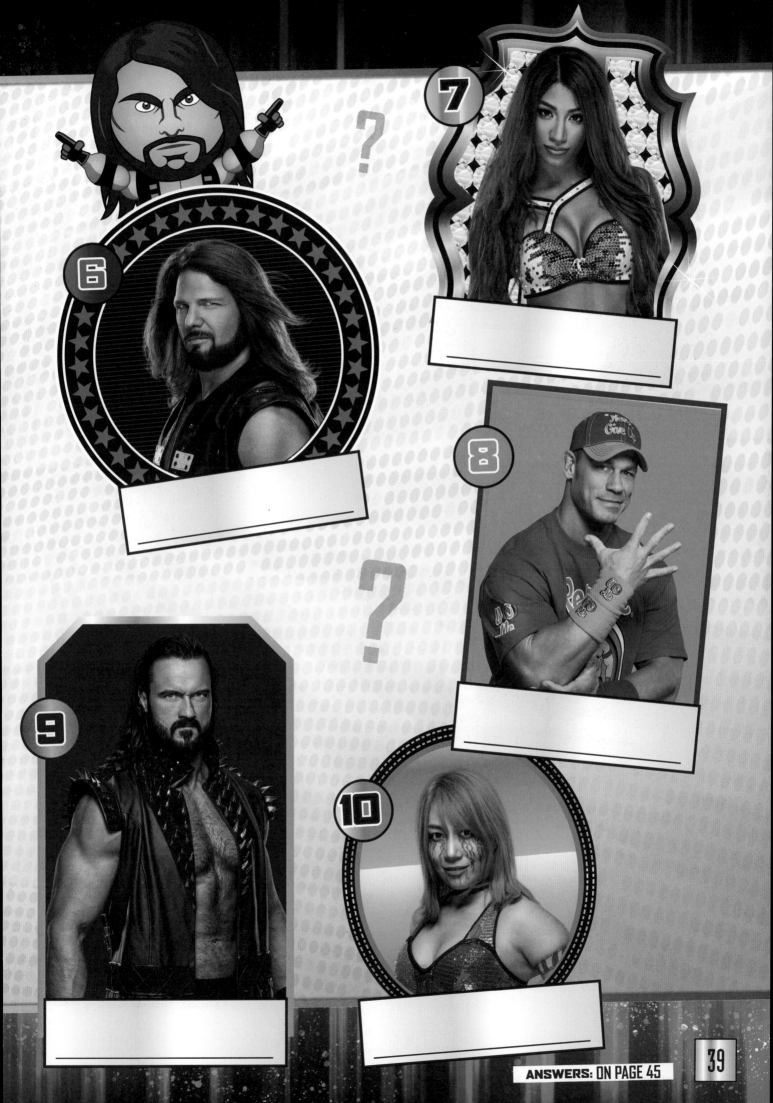

7

6

8

9

10

?

?

ANSWERS: ON PAGE 45

39

FEARSOME FAMILY

Superstars **Roman Reigns** and **The Usos (Jey and Jimmy)** make up a terrifying tag team. Can you work out which jigsaw piece is the correct one to complete the picture?

||| All three Superstars are members of the Anoa'i family. |||

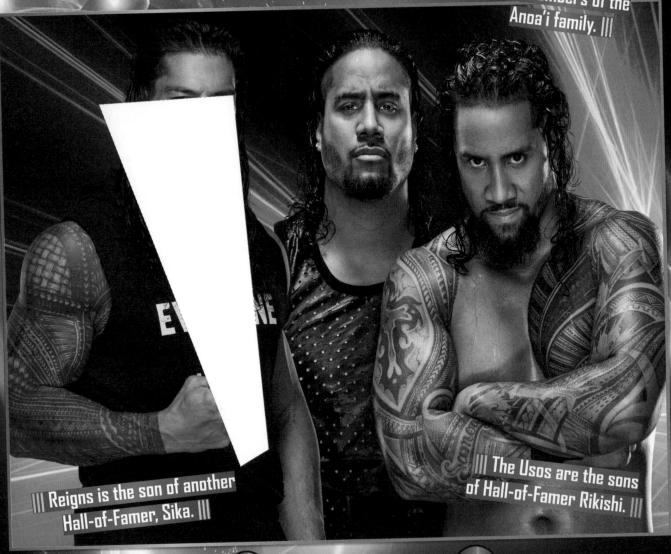

||| Reigns is the son of another Hall-of-Famer, Sika. |||

||| The Usos are the sons of Hall-of-Famer Rikishi. |||

1

2

3

4

||| Reigns and The Usos are first cousins once removed. |||

MEMORY MATCH

It's time to put your memory to the test. Take a few minutes to study the picture and facts on the previous page, then cover it up and **answer the questions below** – without cheating!

ROMAN EMPIRE

1. DOES ROMAN REIGNS HAVE A BEARD?

2. WHICH OF ROMAN'S ARMS IS TATTOOED?

3. WHICH OF THE USOS IS WEARING A VEST TOP?

4. IS ROMAN'S HAIR TIED UP OR HANGING LOOSE?

5. IS ROMAN STANDING IN THE MIDDLE?

6. ARE REIGNS AND THE USOS FIRST COUSINS TWICE REMOVED?

7. WHAT FAMILY DO ALL THREE SUPERSTARS BELONG TO?

8. WHAT IS THE NAME OF ROMAN REIGNS' FATHER?

9. WHAT IS THE NAME OF THE USOS' FATHER?

ANSWERS: ON PAGE 45

THE QUIZ OF LEGENDS

The Superstars on these pages are the most legendary in WWE history. How well do you know them? Answer each statement by ticking **TRUE** or **FALSE**.

1 Bret "Hit Man" Hart's signature move is The Sharpshooter.

☐ TRUE
☐ FALSE

2 "Macho Man" is the nickname for Shawn Michaels.

☐ TRUE
☐ FALSE

3 Andre The Giant is over 7 feet tall.

☐ TRUE
☐ FALSE

4 "Rowdy" Roddy Piper is from Glasgow in Scotland.

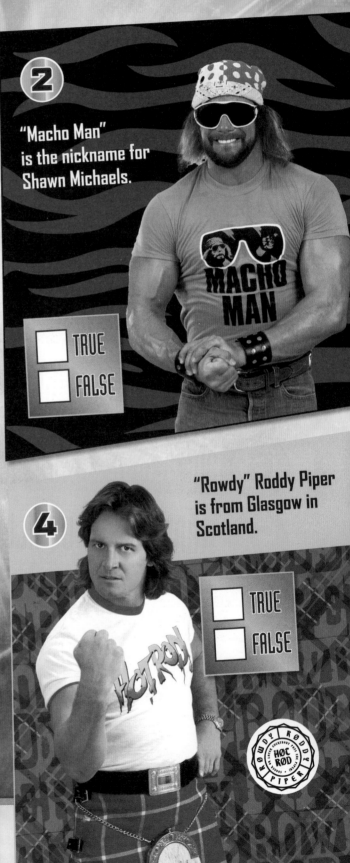

☐ TRUE
☐ FALSE

...ughter
...liss.

☐ TRUE
☐ FALSE

RIC FLAIR
The Nature Boy

6
Shawn Michaels' once wrote his own theme tune.

☐ TRUE
☐ FALSE

7
Ted Dibiase is better known as "Billion Dollar Man".

☐ TRUE
☐ FALSE

8
"Stone Cold" Steve Austin joined WWE in 2016.

☐ TRUE
☐ FALSE

9
Razor Ramon is also know as "The Good Guy".

☐ TRUE
☐ FALSE

10
Sgt. Slaughter's signature move was the Cobra Clutch.

☐ TRUE
☐ FALSE

43

ANSWERS: ON PAGE 45

ANSWERS

Page 9

1. YOU CAN'T SEE ME,
2. HUSTLE, LOYALTY, RESPECT,
3. NEVER GIVE UP

Page 11

Page 13

Page 14

1. QUEEN, **2.** LEGLOCK,
3. VOLLEYBALL, **4.** NATURE BOY,
5. CONQUER

Pages 16-17

7 TIMES
4

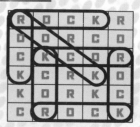

Pages 18-19

RIC & CHARLOTTE FLAIR
(FATHER AND DAUGHTER)
THE ROCK & ROMAN REIGNS
(COUSINS)
BRETT HART & NATALYA
(UNCLE AND NIECE)

Pages 20-21

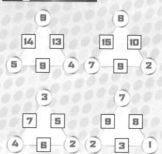

1 AND 4

Page 23

1. JOHN CENA, **2.** ROMAN REIGNS,
3. KANE, **4.** SETH ROLLINS. **5.** BRAUN
STROWMAN, **6.** RANDY ORTON,
7. AJ STYLES, **8.** KEVIN OWENS

Pages 26-27

1. SMACKDOWN, **2.** STRONGEST, **3.** KNOXVILLE
1. FALSE, **2.** TRUE, **3.** TRUE, **4.** FALSE,
5. TRUE, **6.** FALSE, **7.** TRUE, **8.** FALSE

Pages 28-29

1. SMACKDOWN, **2.** UNDERTAKER, **3.** IRELAND,
4. FINN BÁLOR, **5.** RAW, **6.** BECKY LYNCH,
7. ROMAN REIGNS, **8.** CLAYMORE,
9. BRAY WYATT, **10.** "STONE COLD" STEVE AUSTIN

Pages 30-31

8 TIMES
THE BEST THERE IS
SHAWN MICHAELS

H	T	H	A	R	T
T	H	A	R	T	R
T	R	R	H	R	A
R	A	T	R	A	H
A	H	A	R	T	A
H	A	R	T	T	R

Pages 32-33

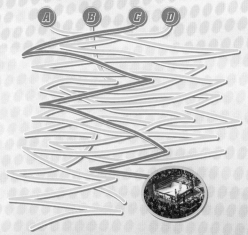

1. SPIDER
2. SAVAGE
3. RANDY
4. BASEBALL
5. BEST
6. ELBOW
7. HOT
8. STATES

A   B   C   D

Pages 34-35

2
1. YES, **2.** NO – THIS WAS SAID BY
THE ROCK, **3.** NO – THIS WAS SAID
BY ULTIMATE WARRIOR, **4.** YES,
5. YES **6.** NO – THIS WAS SAID
BY JOHN CENA, **7.** NO – THIS WAS
SAID BY BIG E

Page 36

v's

Page 37

Pages 38-39

1. PAIGE, **2.** THE FIEND, **3.** KEITH LEE,
4. ROMAN REIGNS, **5.** BECKY LYNCH,
6. AJ STYLES, **7.** SASHA BANKS,
8. JOHN CENA, **9.** DREW MCINTYRE,
10. ASUKA.

Page 40

PIECE NUMBER 2

Page 41

1. YES, **2.** HIS RIGHT, **3.** JIMMY,
4. HANGING LOOSE, **5.** NO
6. NO, ONCE REMOVED,
7. ANOA'I, **8.** SIKA, **9.** RIKISHI

Pages 42-43

1. TRUE, **2.** FALSE – IT'S RANDY SAVAGE,
3. TRUE, **4.** TRUE, **5.** FALSE – IT'S
CHARLOTTE FLAIR, **6.** FALSE – IT'S
MILLION DOLLAR MAN, **7.** TRUE, **8.** FALSE
– HE JOINED BACK IN 1996. **9.** FALSE
– HE'S THE BAD GUY, **10.** TRUE